J-

MORE PRAISE FOR BABYMOUSE!

"A new hero emerges in . . . Babymouse." **—The Bulletin**

"Young readers will happily fall in line." **—Kirkus Reviews**

"The brother-sister creative team hits the mark with humor, sweetness, and characters so genuine they can pass for real kids." **—Booklist**

"Babymouse is spunky, ambitious, and, at times, a total dweeb." **—School Library Journal**

Sing your heart out for **all the BABYMOUSE** books:

BABYMOUSE

THE MUSICAL

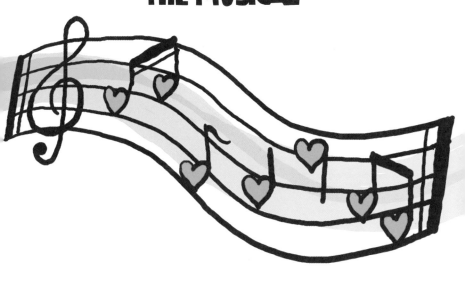

BY JENNIFER L. HOLM & MATTHEW HOLM

RANDOM HOUSE NEW YORK

I HOPE WE WIN A TONY!

Copyright © 2009 by Jennifer Holm and Matthew Holm.

All rights reserved.
Published in the United States by Random House Children's Books,
a division of Random House, Inc., New York.

Random House and colophon are registered trademarks of Random House, Inc.

Visit us on the Web!
www.randomhouse.com/kids
www.babymouse.com

Educators and librarians, for a variety of teaching tools, visit us at
www.randomhouse.com/teachers

Library of Congress Cataloging-in-Publication Data
Holm, Jennifer L.
Babymouse : the musical / by Jennifer & Matthew Holm.
   p.   cm.
Summary: As tryouts for the school musical begin, Babymouse takes the starring role in several imaginary Broadway productions, which also feature her debonair new classmate, Henry the Hedgehog.
ISBN 978-0-375-84388-4 (trade pbk.) — ISBN 978-0-375-93791-0 (lib. bdg.)
1. Graphic novels. [1. Graphic novels. 2. Musicals—Fiction. 3. Theater—Fiction. 4. Imagination—Fiction. 5. Mice—Fiction. 6. Animals—Fiction. 7. School—Fiction.]
I. Holm, Matthew. II. Title.
PZ7.7.H65Bal 2009 [Fic]—dc22 2008010891

MANUFACTURED IN MALAYSIA 10 9 8 7 6 5

One!

CLICK!

Singular sensation!

TAP
TAP
TAP

Every little book she reads.

One!

Thrilling mouse-a-tation!

TRIP!

WHUMP!

OOF!

AUDITIONS FOR SCHOOL MUSICAL!

MUST BE ABLE TO SING **AND** DANCE

YOU SHOULD TRY OUT FOR THE MUSICAL, BABYMOUSE.

13

BRILLIANT! *SIGH.*

SO HOW COME YOU CAN NEVER GET YOUR **OWN** LOCKER OPEN, BABYMOUSE?

HUH?

GO FOR IT, BABYMOUSE. AT LEAST IT'S NOT SQUID TENTACLES.

GRAB!

SWOOSH

WHOA!

SLAM!

19

IN A CAVERN BENEATH THE SCHOOL...

WOW. WHO KNEW THEY HAD CHANDELIERS DOWN HERE?

THE NEXT DAY.

AUDITIONS FOR SCHOOL MUSICAL!

MUST BE ABLE TO SING **AND** DANCE

BABYMOUSE, ARE YOU TRYING OUT FOR THE MUSICAL?

UH...

I BET YOU HAVE BRILLIANT STAGE PRESENCE!

ME?

LATER.

ALL RIGHT, PEOPLE, I WANT A FAIR GAME. NO BALLS TO THE HEAD. STAY LIGHT ON YOUR FEET AND ATTACK LIKE **LIONS!**

PEEP!

LION...

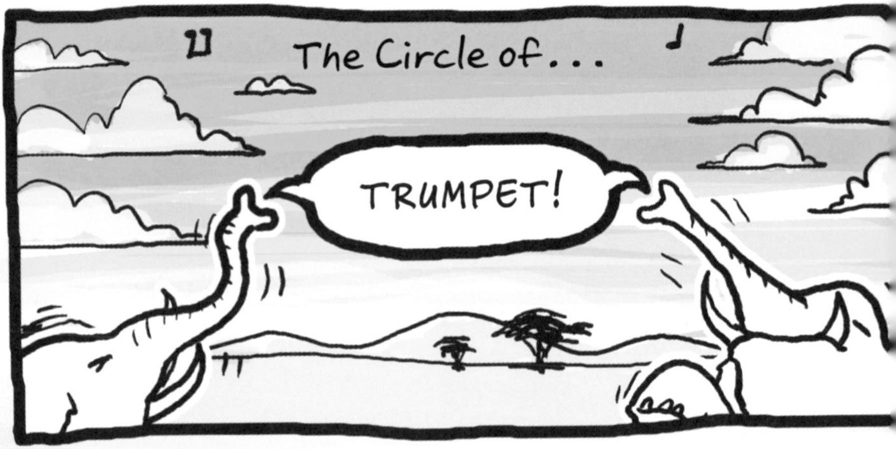
The Circle of . . .
TRUMPET!

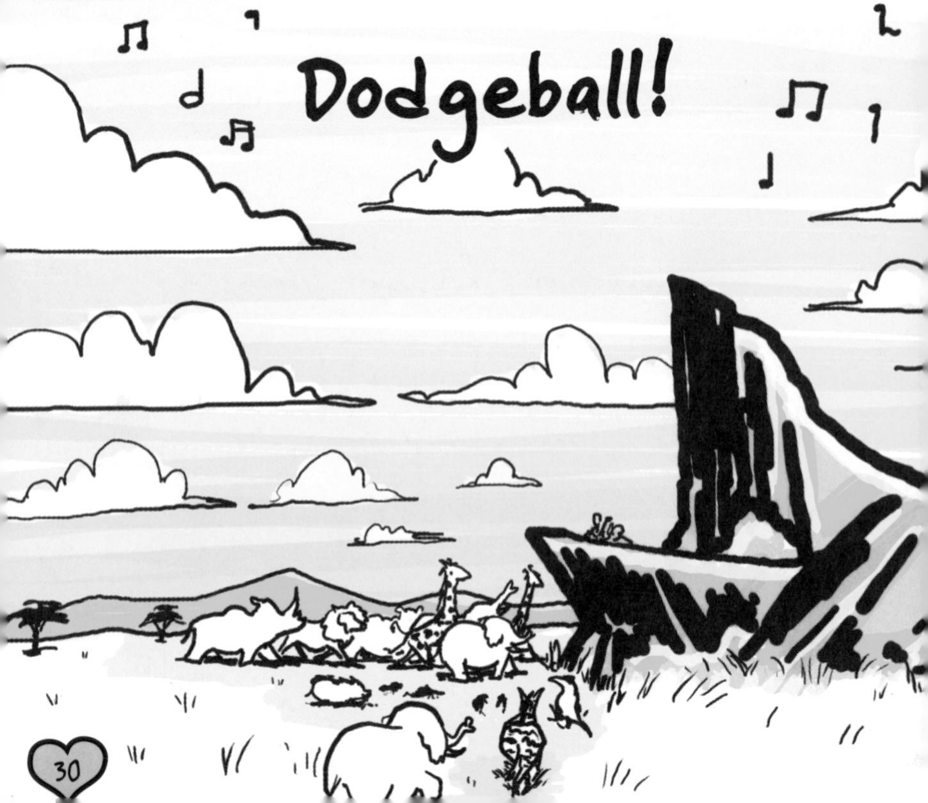
Dodgeball!

32

34

MAYBE **I** SHOULD AUDITION!
HOW ABOUT A LITTLE GILBERT AND SULLIVAN?
AHEM!

I am the very model of a graphic novel narrator.

I have information on the action, scenery, and characters.

I tell the readers when you're in Antarctica or Paris or—

when your locker's trying to ensnare you with its tentacles!

SHEESH!

WHAT A HAM!

36

RABIES!

TOE FUNGUS!

DON'T HOLD YOUR BREATH, BABYMOUSE. I NEVER GET SICK.

BLINK!

CHEER UP, BABYMOUSE. MAYBE A HAIR BALL WILL GET STUCK IN HER THROAT.

SIGH.

43

55

THE NEXT MORNING.

TWIRL

SEE YOU AT REHEARSAL!

FWAP!

I'M NOT GOING.

WHY NOT?

:BLINK!:

UH, JUST THE SALT, BABYMOUSE.

PANT PANT

HERE YOU GO.

I LIKED THE TWO-STEP, BABYMOUSE.

NOBODY APPRECIATES REAL TALENT.

I feel pretty, oh so pretty! I feel pretty and witty and bright! And I pity any mouse who is the understudy tonight!

73

PLACES, EVERYONE! THE SHOW IS ABOUT TO BEGIN!

CLAP CLAP

MAKE SURE MY NEXT COSTUME IS READY, BABYMOUSE!

SHOVE!

74

THIS IS IT, BABYMOUSE! YOUR BIG SHOT AT FAME!

GULP!

BELIEVE IN YOURSELF, BABYMOUSE!

BREAK A LEG!

THAT'S YOUR CUE, BABYMOUSE! GO!

HENRY?

YOU **ARE** TRYING OUT FOR THE NEXT MUSICAL, AREN'T YOU?

ME?

I BET YOU HAVE **BRILLIANT** STAGE PRESENCE!

WHY DON'T YOU COME OVER TO MY HOUSE AFTER SCHOOL AND WE CAN REHEARSE?

WHAT DO YOU THINK OF THAT, BABYMOUSE?

THE FATE OF A DISTANT LAND...

RESTS IN THE HEART

FOOSH!

OF ONE MOUSE.

HELP!

BABYMOUSE: Dragonslayer!

EPIC ADVENTURE COMING FALL 2009!

I'M HERE TO RESCUE YOU!

WOW—SHE LOOKS SERIOUS, FOLKS!